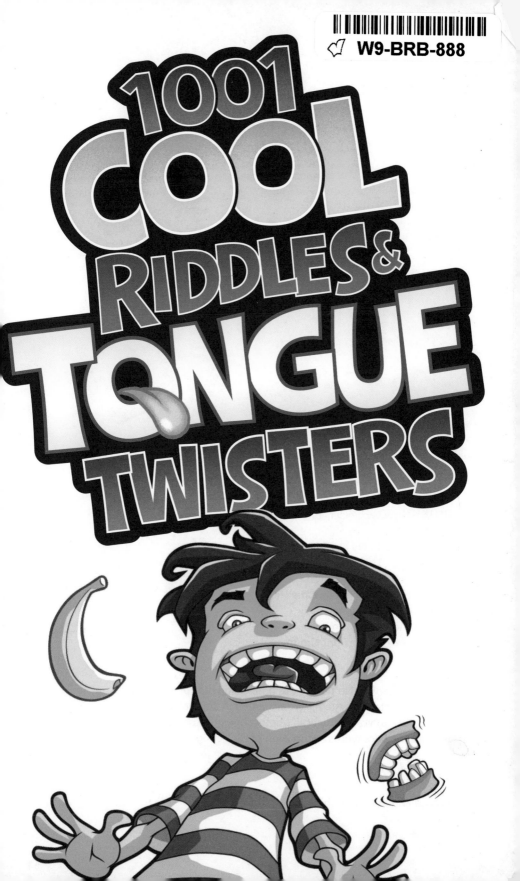

1001 COOL RIDDLES & TONGUE TWISTERS

Published by Hinkler Books Pty Ltd
45–55 Fairchild Street
Heatherton Victoria 3202 Australia
www.hinkler.com.au

© Hinkler Books Pty Ltd 2015

Illustrated by Glen Singleton
Writing and compiling by Katie Hewat
Cover illustration by Rob Kiely
Typesetting by MPS Limited
Prepress by Graphic Print Group

ISBN: 978 1 7436 3844 6

Printed and bound in China

CONTENTS

Animal Absurdities

Riddles

1   **W**hat do well-behaved young lambs say to their mothers?

'Thank-ewe.'

2   **W**hat's grey and can't see well from either end?

A donkey with its eyes shut.

3   **W**hat do elephants play marbles with?

Bowling balls.

4   **W**hat asks but never answers?

An owl.

5 **W**hat's the same size and shape as an elephant but weighs nothing at all?

An elephant's shadow.

6 **W**hat's got six legs and can fly long distances?

Three swallows.

7 **W**hat's black and white and eats like a horse?

A zebra.

8 **W**hen is a car like a frog?

When it is being toad.

9 **H**ow do you spell 'mouse trap' with only three letters?

C A T.

10 What did the buffalo say to his son, when he went away on a long trip?

'Bison.'

11 If a horse loses its tail, where can it get another one?

At a re-tail store.

12 How do you know when it's been raining cats and dogs?

You step into a poodle.

13 How many animals did Moses fit in the Ark?

None, it was Noah's Ark.

14 How do you get down from an elephant?

You don't get down from an elephant; you get down from a duck.

15 **W**hat's bright orange and sounds like a parrot?

A carrot.

16 **W**hat does an octopus wear when it's cold?

A coat of arms.

WASH DAY AT THE OCTOPUS' PLACE

17 **W**hat's the difference between a dark sky and an injured lion?

One pours with rain and the other roars with pain.

18 **W**hat would you get if you crossed a hunting dog with a journalist?

A news hound.

Ralph the Bloodhound gets his Journalism Degree, buys himself a camera and goes chasing movie stars with the paparazzi ...

19 **W**hat happened to the two frogs that caught the same bug at the same time?

They were tongue-tied.

20 **I**f horses wear shoes,
what do camels wear?
Desert boots.

21 **W**hy are dolphins clever?
Because they live in schools.

22 **W**hat do bees do with
their honey?
They cell it.

23 **W**hat do you call a cat who lives in a hospital?
A first aid kit.

24 **W**hat do you call a cat that plays football?
Puss in boots.

25 **W**hat can go as fast as a race horse?

The jockey.

26 **W**hy is the letter 't' important to a stick insect?

Because without it, it would be a sick insect.

27 **W**hy should you be careful playing against a team of big cats?

They might be cheetahs.

28 **I**'m the part of a bird that's not in the sky; I can swim in the ocean and remain dry. What am I?

Its shadow.

WOH THERE! A MINOR BIRD! I nearly stood on the little guy!

29 **W**hich bird never grows up?

The minor bird.

30 **W**hat's the difference between a bird and a fly?

A bird can fly but a fly can't bird.

31   **W**hat is more fantastic than a talking dog?

A spelling bee.

32   **W**hen is a brown dog not a brown dog?

When it's a greyhound.

33   **W**hat do you call a bee that is always complaining?

A grumble bee.

34   **H**ow do you stop a dog from digging up the front yard?

Put it out the back.

35   **W**hy does a tiger have stripes?

So it won't be spotted.

36   **W**hat is a prickly pear?

Two hedgehogs.

37 **H**ow can you tell a dogwood tree?

By its bark.

38 **W**hat do you get if you cross a worm with a baby goat?

A dirty kid.

39 **W**hat kind of sharks never eat women?

Man-eating sharks!

40 **W**hat has four legs and an arm?

A happy lion.

41 **W**hy was the glow-worm unhappy?

Her children weren't very bright.

42 **W**hen is it bad luck to be followed by a big black cat?

When you are a little grey mouse.

43 **W**hy are giraffes good friends to have?

Because they stick their necks out for you.

44 **W**hy was the mother flea so sad?

Because her children were going to the dogs.

45 **W**here do you find a no-legged dog?

Right where you left it.

Here, boy !!!

46 **W**hat's green and red and goes 120 km/h?

A frog in a blender.

47 **W**hat fly has laryngitis?

A horsefly (hoarse fly).

48 **W**hat's black and white and rolls down a hill?

A penguin.

49 **W**hat's black and white and laughs?

The penguin that pushed the other one.

50 **W**hat happened to the horse that swallowed a dollar?

He bucked.

51 **W**hat animal builds his house in the jungle?

A boa constructor.

52 **W**hy do gorillas have big nostrils?

Because they have big fingers.

53 **W**hat has 50 legs and can't walk?

Half a centipede.

54 **W**hat do you get when an elephant stands on your roof?

Mushed rooms.

55 **W**hat do you get if you run a sparrow over with a lawn mower?

Shredded tweet.

56 **W**hat do polar bears get from sitting on the ice too long?

Polaroids.

57   **W**hat's an army of worms called?

An apple corps.

58   **W**hat's the last thing that goes through a bug's mind as it hits a car windscreen?

His bottom.

59   **W**hat do you get when you cross a rooster with a steer?

A cock and bull story.

60   **W**hat's worse than finding a worm in your apple?

Finding half a worm!

61   **W**hat do you get if you pour hot water down a rabbit hole?

Hot cross bunnies.

62 **A** hundred feet in the air and yet my back is still on the ground. What am I?

An upside-down centipede.

63 **W**hat do you get if you sit under a cow?

A pat on the head.

64 **W**here did Noah keep the bees?

In the Ark hives.

65 **W**hich bird can lift the most?

A crane.

66 **W**hy did the lizard cross the road?

To see his flat mate.

67 **W**hat has a foot but no legs?

A snail.

68 **W**hat has four legs and flies?

A dead cat.

69 **W**hat do you call a lion wearing a hat?

A dandy lion.

70 **W**hat is grey, has a tail and a trunk but is not an elephant?

A mouse on vacation.

71 **W**hat do you call a lamb with a machine gun?

Lambo.

72 **W**hy are naughty kids like maggots?

Because they try to wiggle out of everything.

73 **W**hat do you get when you cross an automobile with a household animal?

A carpet.

74 **W**hen do you put a frog in your sister's bed?

When you can't find a mouse.

75 **W**hat are teenage giraffes told when they go on their first date?

'No necking.'

76 **W**hat grows up while growing down?

A duck.

77 **W**hy don't turkeys get invited to dinner parties?

Because they use fowl language.

78 **I**f a rooster laid a brown egg and a white egg, what colour would the chicks be?

Roosters don't lay eggs.

79   **W**hy wasn't the butterfly invited to the dance?

Because it was a moth ball.

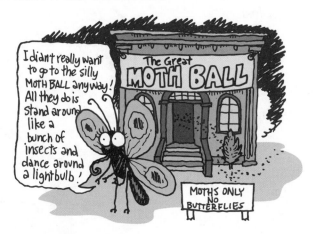

80   **I**f a man carried my burden, he'd break his back. I am not rich, but I always leave silver in my trail. What am I?

A snail.

81   **W**hat part of a fish weighs the most?

The scales.

82   **W**hy do elephants have trunks?

Because they can't fit everything in their handbags.

83   **W**hat do you say when you meet a toad?

'Wart's new?'

84 **W**here do you find elephants?

You don't. They're so big they don't get lost.

85 **W**hat language do birds speak?

Pigeon English.

86 **W**hat is a polygon?

A dead parrot.

I reckon I'm hot on this guy's trail!

87 **W**hat do you have when twenty rabbits step backwards?

A receding hare-line.

88 **Y**ou are in a room with a lemur, a chimpanzee and a gorilla. Which primate in the room is smartest?

You are!

89 **W**hat do you call an amorous insect?

A love bug.

90 **A** monkey, a squirrel and a bird race to the top of a coconut tree. Who reaches the banana first?

None of them. There are no bananas is coconut trees.

91 **W**hy do chickens lay eggs?

Because if they drop them they will break.

92 **W**hat walks on its head all day?

A nail in a horseshoe.

93 **W**here do fish keep their money?

In a river bank.

94 **W**ho always goes to sleep wearing shoes?

A horse.

95 What time is it when an elephant sits on your fence?

Time to get a new fence.

96 Who spends all day at the window, goes to the table for meals and hides at night?

A fly.

97 I have a little house in which I live in all alone. It has no doors or windows, and if I want to go out I must break through the wall. What am I?

A baby bird in an egg.

98 What is the single greatest use of cowhide?

Covering cows.

99 What has four legs and can see just as well from both ends?

A horse with its eyes closed.

Tongue Twisters

100 The thick, slippery snake sneaked and slithered.

101 The fleeing fly finally flew fast.

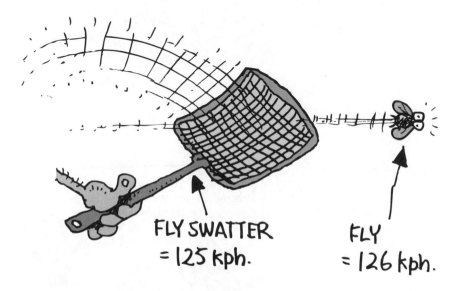

FLY SWATTER
= 125 kph.

FLY
= 126 kph.

102 Four frozen flies were free to flee.

103 The tired turtle tried to tread tenderly.

104   The sleek, shiny shark swam silently.

105   The drinking donkey drank delicately.

106   Ordinarily, ordinary orange orang utans organised orderly outings.

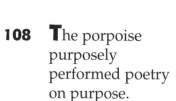

107   Polly parrot wanted wilted peppers.

108   The porpoise purposely performed poetry on purpose.

109   The awkward octopus awkwardly awoke.

110 **P**igeons surely shyly sit on statues.

111 **T**he dog dragged Daisy's dolly for digging.

112 **T**he stinger stung Sheryl with a sharp stab.

113 **P**aulie Bull pulled but Billy Pug bailed.

114 **W**hen Warren Rabbit really wanted he'd rush into his rabbit warren.

Gross and Gory

Riddles

115 What's invisible and smells like carrots?

Bunny farts.

116 What do you call an elephant that never washes?

A smellyphant.

117 What's yellow and smells like bananas?

Monkey vomit.

118 How can you tell when a moth farts?

It flies straight for a second.

Yeee-hah!

119 What's brown and sounds like a bell?

Dung.

120 **W**hat do you give an elephant with diarrhoea?

Plenty of room.

121 **W**hat do you give a sick elephant?

A very big paper bag.

When Nancy said she had a rumble in her tummy... everyone knew just what she meant!

122 **W**hat's a sick joke?

Something that comes up in conversation.

123 **W**hat's the hardest part about sky diving?

The ground.

124 **H**ow do you make a Venetian blind?

Poke his eyes out.

Boy! I could really go for a burger and fries!

You can get mighty hungry just laying around!

125 **H**ow can you tell if a corpse is angry?

It flips its lid.

126 **W**hat do you find up a clean nose?

Fingerprints.

127 **W**hy didn't the man die when he drank poison?

Because he was in the living room.

128 **W**hat's green, has two legs and sits on the end of your finger?

The boogeyman.

129 **W**hat do you do if your nose goes on strike?

Picket!

130 **W**hat do you call the red stuff between an elephant's toes?

A slow explorer.

131 **H**ow did the basketball get wet?

The players dribbled all over it.

132 **H**ow do you make a
tissue dance?

Put some boogie into it.

133 **W**hat is the difference
between broccoli and
boogers?

*Kids don't like to eat
broccoli.*

134 **W**hat did one toilet
say to the other toilet?

'You look a bit flushed!'

135 **W**hat did the first
mate see in the toilet?

The captain's log.

136 **W**hy did the surfer
stop surfing?

Because the sea weed.

137 What happens when the queen burps?

She issues a royal pardon.

138 Why do petrol stations always lock their toilets?

They are afraid someone might clean them.

139 Why did the boy take his own toilet paper to the party?

Because he was a party pooper.

140 Why do they have fences around graveyards?

Everyone is dying to get in.

141 What's green and slimy and hangs from trees?

Giraffe boogers.

142 Why did the toilet paper roll down the hill?

To get to the bottom.

143 What's another name for a snail?

A booger with a crash helmet.

144 **W**hat do you do with crude oil?

Teach it some manners.

145 **H**ow do you keep flies out of the kitchen?

Put a pile of manure in the living room.

146 **W**hat's the difference between a maggot and a cockroach?

Cockroaches crunch more when you eat them.

147 **W**hat's the difference between school lunches and a pile of slugs?

School lunches are in lunch boxes.

148 **W**hat has two grey legs and two brown legs?

An elephant with diarrhoea.

149 **W**hat's yellow, brown and hairy?

Cheese on toast, dropped on carpet.

Tongue Twisters

150 **A** vampire thirstily sucked thick blood.
He glugged, gobbled, gargled and gulped.
He swished, swirled and swallowed.

151 **S**even short, slimy zombies sloshed, slipped and slid
on a shiny, slippery slide.

152 **F**our fighting farty fighters farted frequently while
fighting ferociously.

153 **O**range spew,
red spew,
yellow spew,
blue spew.

154 **P**eter Popov
popped off
presently.

155 The queen quite cleverly created chaos with a steamy stinker.

156 Thick, slimy sticky snot.

157 Gooey poo on Stewie's shoe.

158 Brock's BO brought Bob to tears.

159 Doreen's double Dutch oven disgusted Darren.

160 Really waxy ears are ringing.

161 Jerry's gorbies glowed green.

162 **S**eth's stomach solemnly sent spew spewing.

163 **M**y smelly, slimy, stinky sister's sloppy nappies.

164 **S**weat-soaked smelly armpit stink.

165 **P**loppy Peter's pretty putridly pongy.

166 **F**rank's farts freaked Francine.

167 **S**ammy's sweaty shirt was soaked in sweat.
Silly Sally slipped on Sammy's sloppy sweat.
Simple Simon swam in Sammy's sweat.
Sammy simply said, 'That's wet.'

168 **T**he Blob was a blobby gooey glob.

169 Tongue twisters twist tongues. Twisted tongues taste terrible. Terrible tasting tongues twist tightly. A toast to tightly twisted terrible tasting tongues.

170 Suddenly, Samuel saw snotty Sarah stealing several strands of snot.

171 Bob's big burp blasted barriers.

172 Paul popped his pus-filled pimple.

173 Betty bet Poppy that pro-ballers have BO problems.

174 Girl gargoyle, guy gargoyle, gurgling gluey goo.

175 Eric's earwax was orange, obviously.

176 Girty gurgled good blood and bad blood.

177 Flora's flatulence frighteningly floored Freddy.

178 If Flora farted, Francine fell and Frannie fainted, how foul was Flora's fart?

179 Chucky's chunder had colourful carrot chunks.

180 Octavia's up-chuck was oddly orange.

181 Six snot balls shot past Sally Schnell.

Game On!

Riddles

182 **W**hat is put on the table and cut, but never eaten.
A deck of cards.

183 **W**hat does every winner lose in a race?
Their breath.

184 **W**hat stories are told by basketball players?
Tall stories.

185 **W**hy did all the bowling pins go down?
They were on strike.

186 **W**hat has 22 legs and two wings but cannot fly?
A soccer team.

187 **W**hich goalkeeper can jump higher than a crossbar?
All of them – a crossbar can't jump!

188 **W**hy did the footballer take a piece of rope onto the pitch?
He was the skipper.

When you've finished skipping... Can we get on with the game?

189 **W**hat part of a football ground smells the best?
The scenter spot.

190 **W**hen are babies like basketball players?
When they dribble.

Even basketballers start off by dribbling!

191 **W**hat do you call a cat that plays football?
Puss in boots.

192 **W**hat illness do martial artists get?
Kung flu.

193 **W**hy were the arrows nervous?
Because they were all in a quiver.

194 **W**ho was the fastest runner in the whole world?
Adam, because he was the first in the human race.

195 **W**hat race is never run?
A swimming race.

196 **W**hat did one bowling ball say to the other?
'Don't stop me, I'm on a roll!'

197 **W**hat's the best way to win a race?

Run faster than everyone else.

198 **W**here do old
bowling balls end
up?

In the gutter.

This sort of gutter is no place for an old bowling ball!

199 **W**hat was the fly
doing in the lady's
soup?

Backstroke.

200 **W**hy was the boxer
known as Picasso?

Because he spent all his time on the canvas.

201 **W**hy don't
grasshoppers go to
football matches?

*They prefer cricket
matches.*

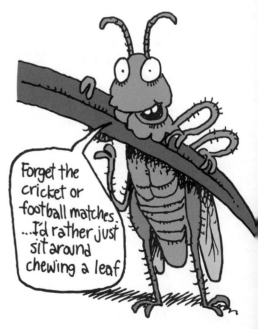

Forget the cricket or football matches... I'd rather just sit around chewing a leaf

202 **W**hat is the smelliest
sport?

Ping pong!

203 **W**hy aren't football stadiums built in outer space?
Because there is no atmosphere!

204 **W**hy is tennis such a noisy game?
Because everyone raises a racket.

205 **W**hy did the bicycle keep falling over?
Because it was two tired.

206 **W**hen is it handy to have toes?
When you go to a foot ball.

207 **W**hat is harder to catch the faster you run?
Your breath.

Tongue Twisters

208 **W**ayne likes white-water rafting after work.

There's not even a river around here!

Tired of catching the bus, Wayne decides to white-water raft his way home.

209 **B**ree's billiards brilliance bewildered Brooke.

210 **A** broad bloke boxed blindly.

211 **T**revor's trophy for table tennis triumph was terrific.

212 **B**oris beat Barney in breaststroke.

213 Right hook, left hook, uppercut, left jab.

214 Sprinting Sally hurdled hurdles.

215 Athletic athletes are, at least, athletically athletic.

216 The athletes decided to discuss discus delegations.

217 Shot-puts squash feet.

218 Callum's karate class created classic karate kicks.

219 The fighters frightened fans fighting a frighteningly fearsome fight.

220 The wild, wide wrestler went whacko.

221 The quick quiet cricketer requested cricketing competition.

222 Stanley loved sitting, sipping soda on his sofa, seeing stunned skiers stacking in snow. Seriously, Stanley loved seeing sporting slip-ups.

223 Prince Paul played polo pretty poorly.

224 Wrestlers wearing lycra are really weird.

225 The good golfer's green golf glove.

226 Relay runners run relays really regularly.

227 Paul played plinky, plonky ping-pong.

228 Barbara's barbed-wire barbell.

229 **F**loundering Freya felt the burn.

230 **D**arren dropped a dumbbell on his dad.

231 **S**andy skipped swiftly.

232 **B**iceps, triceps, thigh sets, high reps.

233 **S**andy surely showed super cycling style.

234 **T**im took training tips and the training tips Tim took taught Tim to train.

235 **T**ony tried Terry's treadmill.

236 **T**he golfer gripped the golf grip grudgingly.

237 **S**arah's sixth cycling session surely sucked.

238 **B**obby the baseballer briefly broke baseball bats by bashing baseballs.

239 **P**ush-ups, press-ups, pull-ups, sit-ups.

240 Peggy Babcock puffed and panted in pump class.

241 Skeeter's skiing school skied slowly.

Perhaps if I'd gone to a faster ski school, that avalanche might not have caught up with me.

242 Brad's bulging biceps burst.

243 Stewart slipped and tripped on the steep slope he trekked.

All it took to start an avalanche was for Stewart to slip and trip...

244 Brandon's black boxing gloves broke bashing punching bags.

The Five Senses

Riddles

245 What can you hear but not see and only speaks when it is spoken to?

An echo.

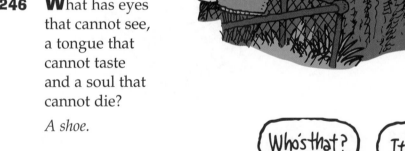

246 What has eyes that cannot see, a tongue that cannot taste and a soul that cannot die?

A shoe.

247 What is there more of the less you see?

Darkness.

248 What can you hold without touching?

Your breath.

249 **W**hy did the Invisible Man's wife understand him so well?

Because she could see right through him.

250 **W**hat can you hold but never touch?

A conversation.

251 **W**hat kind of music do fathers like to sing?

Pop music.

252 **W**hat did the parents say to their son who wanted to play drums?

'Beat it!'

253 **W**hat did one ear say to the other ear?

'Between you and me, we need a haircut.'

254 **W**hat can be caught but never seen?

A remark.

255 **W**hat did the ear 'ear?

Only the nose knows.

256 **W**hat tastes better than it smells?

A tongue.

257 **Y**ou can touch me, but not see me. You can throw me out, but not away. What am I?

Your back.

258 **W**hy should you never tell secrets in a grocery store?

Because the corn has ears, potatoes have eyes and beanstalk.

259 **W**hy do farts smell?

So that deaf people can appreciate them too.

260 **W**hat did the floor say to the desk?

I can see your drawers.

261 What do you think when you see a monster?

I hope he hasn't seen me.

262 The person who makes it doesn't need it, the person who buys it doesn't use it and the person who uses it can't see or hear it. What is it?

A coffin.

263 What kind of music do zombies like best?

Soul.

264 What did the digital clock say to its mother?

Look Mum, no hands!

265 **W**hat smells funny?

Clown poo.

266 **W**ho is the smelliest person in the world?

King Pong.

267 **W**hat has eyes but cannot see?

A potato.

268 **S**ay my name and I disappear. What am I?

Silence.

269 **W**hat's the difference between an oral thermometer and a rectal thermometer?

The taste.

Tongue Twisters

270 **F**ergus felt furry fungus.

271 **L**arry liked licking yellow lollies.

272 **H**igh notes, low notes, fast notes, slow notes, loud notes, soft notes, big nose, no nose.

273 **T**revor's triangle tinkled and tingled.

274 Seth's breath smelled like death.

275 Which wise guy's eyes spied the high-priced prize?

276 The selfish elf ate shellfish.

277 Ten top-notch cops felt fob watch knobs.

278 The deer's ears clearly hear another deer's fairly near.

279 Freddy's feet smelled foul.

280 The brilliant big brass band played beautifully.

281 Sheila said she smelled Schmidt shaving.

282 Terry tastes twelve turnips, turning Terry's tongue numb.

283 Yola loves yummy gumbo.

284 Simon sang several sweet-sounding songs.

285 **A** small, steamy smell silently slipped out.

286 **C**hase chews cod. Cows chew cod. If cows chase Chase, is a Chase a cod-chewing cow?

287 **T**he crazy composer caused chaos, creating cringe-worthy compositions.

288 **C**an the toucan touch two tin cans?

289 **M**orose music makes Margaret mournful.

290 Kim counted colours she could see on Shaun's couch.

291 Brad's bassoon broke, bruising Brad badly.

292 The drummer dumbly decided to drum at dawn.

293 Horace hid when he heard Herod honking.

294 Violent violinist.

295 The string section suddenly went on strike, sending shockwaves shooting through the symphony.

296 After the opera, Owen often opted for orange juice.

297 Stacey baked stinky scones.

298 Muriel miraculously made magical music. Actually, Muriel's miraculously magical music was marvellous.

299 Trevor terribly trumpeted till Trixie trampled Trevor's trumpet.

Crazy Critters & Cool Characters

Riddles

300 **W**hat would you call Superman if he lost all his powers?

Man.

301 **W**hat did one angel say to the other angel?

'Halo.'

302 **W**ho is scared of wolves and swears?

Little Rude Riding Hood.

303 **W**here do you find giant snails?

At the ends of their fingers.

304 **H**ow did the Vikings send messages?

By Norse code.

305 **W**hat is big, red and eats rocks?

A big, red rock eater.

306 **W**hich of the witch's friends eats the fastest?

The goblin.

307 **W**hat's the closest thing to silver?

The Lone Ranger's bottom.

308 **W**hat is Dracula's favourite fruit?

Necktarines.

309 **W**hat do Alexander the Great and Kermit the Frog have in common?

The same middle name!

310 **W**hy was Thomas Edison able to invent the light bulb?

Because he was very bright.

311 **W**hy did Dracula take medicine?

To stop his coffin.

312 **W**hy did the vampire go to the orthodontist?

To improve his bite.

313 **W**hat's the difference between Santa Claus and a warm dog?

Santa wears the suit, but the dog just pants.

314 **W**hy did Henry VIII have so many wives?

He liked to chop and change.

315 **W**ho steals from her Grandma's house?

Little Red Robbin Hood.

316 **W**hy is the vampire so unpopular?

Because he is a pain in the neck.

317 What kind of cheese do monsters eat?

Monsterella!

318 During which battle was Lord Nelson killed?

His last one.

319 What did Cinderella say when her photos didn't arrive?

'Some day my prints will come.'

320 Who delivers Christmas present to the wrong houses?

Santa Flaws.

321 What do monsters have mid-morning?

A coffin break.

322 What did Santa Claus's wife say during the thunderstorm?

'Come and look at the rain, dear.'

323 What job does Dracula have with the Transylvanian baseball team?

He's the bat boy.

324 Who was the father of the Black Prince?

Old King Coal.

325 How did Noah steer the Ark at night?

He switched on the floodlights.

326 Why did the young vampire follow his dad's profession?

Because it was in his blood.

327 What's the name of a clever monster?

Frank Einstein.

328 Which bus could sail the oceans?

Columbus.

329 What did the cannibal say to the explorer?

'Nice to eat you.'

330 What do you get if you cross a skunk with a bear?

Winnie the Pooh.

331 What does a monster call his parents?

Dead and Mummy.

332 **W**hy do witches get good bargains?

They're good at haggling.

333 **W**hy did the Cyclops give up teaching?

Because he only had one pupil.

334 **W**hy don't cannibals eat comedians?

Because they taste funny.

335 **W**hat feature do witches love on their computers?

The spell-checker.

336 **W**hat do you call a witch that lives at the beach?

A sand witch!

337 **W**hat does a ghost read every day?

His horrorscope.

338 **W**hat did King Kong say when his sister had a baby?

'Well, I'll be a monkey's uncle!'

339 **W**here does Dracula wash?

In a bloodbath.

340 **W**hat do vampires cross the sea in?

Blood vessels.

341 **W**hy did the zombie decide to stay in his coffin?

He felt rotten.

342 **W**hen do ghosts usually appear?
Just before someone screams.

343 **W**here does Dracula go fishing?
In a bloodstream.

344 **W**hat did the witch say to the vampire?
'Get a life!'

345 **W**hat do you get when you cross a computer with a vampire?
Love at first byte.

346 **H**ow do monsters like their eggs?
Terrifried.

347 Snow White and the Seven Dwarfs were having dinner. The dwarfs asked for more food so Snow White got them some. How many seconds did she take?

Seven.

348 What does a monster eat after he's been to the dentist?

The dentist.

349 What do sea monsters eat?

Fish and ships.

350 What do you do with a blue monster?

Try to cheer him up a bit.

351 Who is the best dancer at a monster party?

The boogie man.

352 What should you take if a monster invites you to dinner?

Someone who can't run as fast as you.

353 Why isn't the Abominable Snowman scared of people?

Because he doesn't believe in them.

354 What does a monster mummy say to her kids at dinnertime?

'Don't chew with someone in your mouth.'

355 Why did the monster eat his music teacher?

Because his Bach was worse than his bite.

356 What's a witch's favourite school subject?

Spelling.

357 **O**n which day do monsters eat people?

Chewsday.

358 **W**hat do ghosts use to type letters?

A type-frighter.

359 **W**hy are Cyclops couples happy together?

Because they always see eye to eye.

360 **W**hat does a boy monster do when a girl monster rolls her eyes at him?

He rolls them back to her.

361 **W**hy do ghosts hate rain?

It dampens their spirits.

362 **W**hat do you call a good-looking, kind and considerate monster?

A complete failure.

363 **W**hy don't ghosts bother telling lies?

Because you can see right through them.

364 **W**hat do you call the winner of a monster beauty contest?

Ugly.

365 **W**hat type of horses do monsters ride?

Night mares.

366 **W**hat do you call a fairy that hasn't taken a bath?

Stinkerbell.

367 **W**hat weapon was most feared by medieval knights?

A can opener.

368 **H**ow does a yeti feel when it gets a cold?

Abominable.

369 **W**hat's green, sits in the corner and cries?

The Incredible Sulk.

370 **I**f you crossed the Loch Ness monster with a shark, what would you get?

Loch jaws.

371 **W**hat did the skeleton say to the twin witches?

Which witch is which?

372 **H**ow many witches does it take to change a light bulb?

Just one, but she changes it into a toad.

373 **W**here do skeletons go swimming?

In the dead sea.

374 **W**hat game do young ghosts love?

Hide and shriek.

375 **H**ow can you tell what a ghost is getting for its birthday?

By feeling its presents.

376 **W**hat illness does a ghost get from eating Christmas decorations?

Tinselitis.

377 **W**hat should you say when you meet a ghost?

'How do you boo, sir?'

378 **W**hat does a vampire never order at a restaurant?

Stake.

379 **W**hy didn't the skeleton go to the dance?

He had no body to go with.

380 **H**ow do you make a skeleton laugh?

Tickle his funnybone.

381 **D**o zombies have trouble getting dates?

No, they can usually dig someone up.

Tongue Twisters

382 **M**allory the mermaid mostly made mischief.

383 **A** pixie presently picked a perfect present.

384 **M**ermaids mainly mingle in lagoons.

385 **C**lara cleverly created classic car tricks.

386 **T**he greedy giant ground bones.

387 **G**rant the giant generally jogged gratefully.

When Grant jogged, the Earth shook.

388 **T**he gabbling, gargling goblin gobbled and gargled.

389 **T**he braggin', arrogant, boastin' dragon.

390 **B**read grinding bones.

391 **S**lick Trixie, the tricky pixie, picked sticks.

392 **A** werewolf was really wary of rabies.

393 Michael's mighty mystical magic manipulated Maxine.

394 Casting and conjuring and creating confusion, illuminating and inventing and instigating illusion.

395 Trudy tried teaching Tyler trickery.

396 Wally wished he was a wizard. Why did Wally wish for wizardry? Really, what Wally wanted was really wicked wizard wear.

397 Which wicked witch was wickedly wicked?

398 Five fairies flipped five flapjacks.

399 A whacky wizard with white whiskers waved his wand.

400 The wry wizard regularly worked on wand waving.

401 The sorcerer practised prickly imprisoning potions privately; practising privately perfected potions perfectly.

402 The alien alliance allowed acrobat eating.

403 The grinning gargoyle greedily gobbled green grapes.

404 Horrid Harriet hated Halloween.
Horrid Harriet found Halloween harrowing.
Horrid Harriet had had it with Halloween,
So Horrid Harriet holidayed in Hawaii.

405 Frankenstein found France frustrating.

406 Ghastly ghosts and grinning ghouls.

407 A werewolf's whiskers rarely waver.

408 Good ghosts generally greet guests jovially.

409 Which witch doctor rain danced?

Perfectly Prehistoric

Riddles

410 **W**hat do you get when a dinosaur skydives?
A big hole.

411 **W**hy are old dinosaur bones kept in a museum?
Because they can't find any new ones.

412 **W**hat do you get if you cross a dinosaur with a vampire?
A blood shortage.

I vant to sark your blurd...

413 How do dinosaurs pass exams?
With extinction.

414 What do you get if you give a dinosaur a pogo stick?
Big holes in your driveway.

415 What do you call a dinosaur that destroys everything in its path?
Tyrannosaurus Wrecks.

416 What do you call a dinosaur that's a noisy sleeper?
Brontosnorus.

417 What do you call a blind dinosaur?
Do-ya-think-he-saurus.

418 **W**hat does a Triceratops sit on?

Its Tricera-bottom!

419 **W**hat's worse than a Tyrannosaurus with a toothache?

A Diplodocus with a sore throat.

420 **W**hat do you get if you cross a dinosaur with a dog?

A very nervous postman.

421 **W**hy don't more dinosaurs join the police force?

They can't hide behind billboards.

422 **W**hat did the egg say to the dinosaur?

'You're egg-stinct.'

423 **W**hy didn't the dinosaur cross the road?

Because roads weren't invented.

424 **W**hy couldn't the long-necked dinosaur see?

Because his head was in the clouds.

425 **W**hat do you call a group of people who dig for dinosaur bones?

A skeleton crew.

426 **W**hat do you call a scared Tyrannosaurus?

A nervous rex.

427 **W**hat's extinct and works in rodeos?

Broncosaurus.

428 What do you call a dinosaur eating a taco?
Tyrannosaurus Mex.

429 When did the last dinosaur die?
After the second-last dinosaur.

430 What do you call a 100-million-year-old dinosaur?
A fossil.

431 What do dinosaurs put on their floors?
Rep-tiles.

432 What's the hardest part of making dinosaur stew?
Finding a pot big enough to hold the dinosaur.

433 **W**hy did the baby dinosaur get arrested?

Because he took the bus home.

434 **W**hat has a spiked tail, plates on its back and 16 wheels?

A Stegosaurus on roller skates.

Tongue Twisters

435 **A** brachiosaurus bellowed with bronchitis.

436 **B**ronwyn bathed the baby brontosaurus in blue bathwater.

437 **T**he fabulous fabrosaurus fabricated fabulously.

438 **T**wo tricky trilobites tickled Trixie.

439 The terribly tiring Pterydactyl was tragically trapped.

440 Saltasaurus shins should be shaved and saved.

441 The dopey dinosaur drank and dived and drowned.

442 Warren wanted a real wheel to do real wheelies;
What Warren really wanted was a real wheel.
Warren wished wheels were real,
But for cavemen wheels weren't real.

443 The saber-tooth slayed a sleuth.

444 The creepy caveman crept quite creepily.

445 The spiky stegosaurus sipped a soda.

446 The tricky triceratops tripped a tyrannosaurus.

447 The brown brontosaurus borrowed bright but bland books.

448 Manny was a whale while Sammy was a mammoth.

449 Naughty Neanderthals neatly gnawed a nifty numbat.

450 The itchy Iguanodon insists on eating Iggy's insects.

451 Fred found freaky fossils that fuelled his fire for finding facts.

452 The bootblack brought the Brachiosaur's black boot back.

453 Sneaky sauropods eat selfish shellfish.

454 Shy Styracosaurus sometimes sheds a single shiny tear.

455 **V**era the vivacious Velociraptor visits Vic with vigour.

456 **A**n affable Afrovenator aptly ate an apple after every act.

457 **C**an Camarasaurus catch a crafty Camaro?

458 **S**ixty-seven thick, thoughtless, sick stegosauruses stuck spikes in twenty-two trapped tyrannosauruses.

459 **S**tewie the stegosaurus slept soundly; Stewie the stegosaurus snored solidly.

Tough and Tricky

Riddles

460 **W**hat's easier to give than receive?
Criticism.

461 **W**hat kind of dress can never be worn?
Your address.

462 **W**hat's the last thing you take off before bed?
Your feet off the floor.

463 **W**hat can go up a chimney down, but not down a chimney up?
An umbrella.

464 What starts working only when it's fired?

A rocket.

465 What is always coming but never arrives?

Tomorrow.

466 What stays in the corner but travels all around the world?

A postage stamp.

467 What do you put in a barrel to make it lighter?

A hole.

468 What comes down but never goes up?

Rain.

469 **W**hat gets wet the more you dry?

A towel.

470 **W**hat sort of ring is always square?

A boxing ring.

471 **W**hat kind of bow can't be tied?

A rainbow.

472 **W**hat runs all around a pasture but never moves?

A fence.

473 **I** am tall when I'm young and short when I'm old, what am I?

A candle.

474 What goes up and down but never moves?

A flight of stairs.

475 Which candle burns longer, a red one or a green one?

Neither. They both burn shorter.

476 What belongs to you but is used more by other people?

Your name.

477 What's always taken before you get it?

Your picture.

478 Poor people have me.
Rich people need me.
If you eat me you die.
What am I?

Nothing.

479 **W**hat can you give away but also keep?

A cold.

480 **W**hat can run but can't walk?

A river.

481 **B**etty rode into town on Friday, and rode out again two days later, on Friday. How?

Friday was the horse's name.

482 **I**f a yellow house is made of yellow bricks and a red house is made of red bricks, what is a green house made of?

Glass.

483 **W**hat goes up and does not come down?

Your age.

484 I only point in one direction, but I guide people around the world. What am I?

A compass.

485 What has a head and a tail but no legs?

A coin.

486 What do you call someone who doesn't have all their fingers on one hand?

Normal. You have fingers on both hands.

487 What was the highest mountain in the world before Mt Everest was discovered?

Mt Everest.

488 What is higher without the head than with it?

A pillow.

489 Take off my skin and I won't cry, but you will. What am I?

An onion.

490 What can you draw without a pencil or paper?

The blinds.

491 What runs down the street but has no legs?

The kerb.

492 What has holes but still holds water?

A sponge.

493 What goes up when rain comes down?

An umbrella.

494 What flies all day but never goes anywhere?

A flag.

495 What goes around the house and in the house but never touches the house?

The sun.

496 The more of these you take, the more you leave behind.

Footsteps.

497 What is brown when you buy it, red when you use it, and black when you throw it away?

Firewood.

498 Everyone has one and they can't lose it. What is it?

A shadow.

499 **W**hat has many rings but no fingers?

A telephone.

500 **W**hat has two legs but can't walk?

A pair of pants.

501 **W**hat US state is round on both sides and high in the middle?

Ohio.

502 **W**hat kind of ship never sinks?

Friendship.

503 **W**hy did the bungee jumper take a vacation?

Because he was at the end of his rope.

504 **W**hy are good intentions like people who faint?

They both need carrying out.

505 **W**hat is always running but never gets anywhere?

A refrigerator.

506 **W**hen is a door not a door?

When it is ajar.

507 **W**hat's a liquid that won't freeze?

Hot water.

508 **W**hat has two hands, no fingers, stands still and goes?

A clock.

509 **W**hat gets bigger and bigger the more you take away from it?

A hole.

510 **H**ow can a pocket be empty but still have something in it?

It can have a hole in it.

511 **I**n a one-storey pink house with pink windows, pink walls, pink doors and pink floors lived a girl with a pink cat which even had pink paws. What colour were the stairs?

There were no stairs. It was a one-storey house.

512 **A** dad and his son had an accident and were taken to different hospitals. Upon seeing the boy, his surgeon said, 'I can't operate on you. You're my son.' How is that possible?

The surgeon was the boy's mother.

513 **W**hat has no legs but is always walking?

A pair of shoes.

514 I can breathe and I will eat what you feed me, but if you give me water I will die. What am I?

A fire.

515 You are lost in a cold dark cave. You have a match, a kerosene lamp and a candle. Which do you light first?

The match.

516 A man was driving his truck without his lights on and the moon was not out, yet he still managed to spot a rabbit run out on the road. How?

It was daylight.

517 If an electric train is travelling south and the wind is blowing north, in which direction would the smoke travel?

There is no smoke from an electric train.

518 What has an eye but cannot see?

A needle.

519 **W**hat is the only certain way you can double your money?

Look at it in the mirror.

520 **S**unday, Tim and Tom had lunch and one of them paid the bill. It wasn't Tim or Tom, so who was it?

Their friend Sunday.

521 **W**hat has a bed but never sleeps, can run but never walks and a bank but no money?

A river.

522 **W**hat loses its head in the morning but gets it back at night?

A pillow.

523 **W**hat has teeth but cannot eat?

A comb.

524 **W**hat sort of person stands around making faces all day?

A watchmaker.

525 **I** have keys but no locks. I have space but no room. You can enter but not go inside. What am I?

A keyboard.

526 **W**hat goes around and around the wood but never goes into the wood?

The bark of a tree.

527 **I** always tell the truth and I copy everything I see. What am I?

A mirror.

528 **W**here do you find roads without cars, forests without trees and towns without houses?

On a map!

529 **W**hat question can you never honestly answer yes to?

Are you asleep?

530 **W**ho is your mother's brother's brother-in-law?

Your dad.

531 **W**hy can't someone living to the north of a river be buried to the south of the river?

Because they are still alive.

532 **W**hat is better than the best thing and worse than the worst thing?

Nothing.

533 **W**hat has no beginning, end or middle?

A doughnut.

534 What grows up while growing down?

A duckling.

535 What do you throw out when you need to use it, and take it back when you don't need it anymore?

An anchor.

536 Forward I am heavy, backward I am not. What am I?

A ton.

537 I am lighter than air but even a million men couldn't lift me up. What am I?

A bubble.

538 What runs across the floor without legs?

Water.

539 **W**hat stays where it is even after it goes off?

An alarm clock.

540 **I** have an eye but cannot see, and am strong and fast but have no limbs. What am I?

A hurricane.

541 **A** box without hinges, lock or key, but a golden treasure lies in me. What am I?

An egg.

542 **I**t's been around for thousands of years but is never more than a month old. What is it?

The moon.

543 **W**hat kind of coat can you put on only when it's wet?

A coat of paint.

544 **W**hat weighs more, a kilo of lead or a kilo of feathers?

They both weigh the same.

545 **B**rothers and sisters I have none, but that man's father is my father's son. Who is that man?

My son.

546 **I**f you have me you want to share me, but if you share me you haven't got me. What am I?

A secret.

547 **W**hat creature walks on four legs when young, two legs when it grows up and three legs when it's old?

A person. Babies crawl, adults walk and elderly people use a cane.

548 **T**here is a green house that contains a white house that contains a pink house which contains lots of babies. What is it?

A watermelon.

549 I am mined and then shut up in a wooden case from which I am never released, and yet I am used by lots of people. What am I?

A pencil lead.

550 What is something you can keep after giving it to someone else?

Your word.

551 When I do it up it walks but when I loosen it, it stops.

A sandal.

552 You can draw me, shoot me and load me but I'm made of nothing. What am I?

A blank.

553 There are many different types but the one you pick doesn't do its job. What is it?

A lock.

554 **W**hat is bought in yards and worn by feet?

Carpet.

555 **I**'m measured in temperature (degrees) and time (minutes and seconds), but have neither. What am I?

Longitude and latitude.

556 **I**f a woman is born in China, grows up in Australia, lives in America and dies in London, what is she?

Dead.

557 **A** king, queen, and two twins all lay in a large room. How are there no adults in the room?

They are all beds.

Tongue Twisters

558 Toy boat (this one looks easy, but say it ten times fast!).

559 Polly peddled Polish sausage.

560 Huge imps sink ships, pink chimps use shrinks.

561 Theoretically, the thirteenth shopfront shouldn't shut.

562 Neal nearly kneeled nearby.

563 **H**arry hurriedly hopped happily.

564 **A** big bug bit a bold bald bear.

565 **L**eft leg, right leg, red leg, yellow leg.

566 **T**he poet poetically promised prime political poetry.

567 **W**endy whispered, Yanni yelled, Ryan roared.
Wendy whispered, Yanni yelled, Ryan roared.
Wendy roared, Yanni whispered, Ryan yelled.
Wendy, Yanni, Ryan yelled, whispered roared.

568 **S**loppy Salina's slippers sadly slipped, sending Salena sliding and slipping.

569 **M**ak met Mike; Mike met Mak;
Mike and Mak met Matt;
Mike, Mak and Matt met Mark;
Mike, Mak, Matt and Mark met Bob.

570 **F**rieda's frantically funny face froze when the westerly wind wafted.

571 **W**iley Wilma Wilmington was wilfully wilfull.

572 **I**n general, in January, Jenny generally generalised.

573 The freezing freezer froze fast.
The fast freezing freezer feels frozen.
The frozen freezer finally defrosted.

574 Barry brought
brilliant butter.

575 Troy Boy
bought Joy soy
with joy.

576 Black background,
brown background,
blue background.

577 Six thick thistles stick.

578 **S**ally's sore sore sure was sore.

579 **W**ally wasn't really whimsical;
Wally wandered what whimsical was.
Witty was what Wally wanted,
And witty was what Wally resoundingly was.

580 **A**n imaginary menagerie manager imagined
managing many menageries.

581 **R**ed lorries,
yellow lollies.

582 **W**ally wore an
Irish wristwatch.
When wound,
Wally's Irish
wristwatch
worked well.

583 'Sure, Samantha,' shy Shelley said shyly.
She certainly shook and seemed to shimmy.
Samantha smiled and served shanks.
'Thanks,' said Shelley.

584 Which witch wished which wicked wish?

585 Unique New York.

586 Six sharp smart sharks.

587 She sifted thistles through her thistle sifter.

588 A box of biscuits, a batch of mixed biscuits.

589 Peter Piper picked a peck of pickled peppers. If Peter Piper picked a peck of pickled peppers, where's the peck of pickled peppers Peter Piper picked?

590 She sells seashells by the seashore. The sea shells that she sells are seashore shells I'm sure.

591 Rubber baby buggy bumpers.

592 Round the rugged rocks the ragged rascal ran.

593 A boy stoat stole Troy's toy boat.

594 Are our oars oak?

595 Fred fed Ned bread; Ned fed Fred bread.

596 Girl apes gripe about Greek grapes.

597 Should Stu choose the shoes he chews?

598 I slit the sheet and on the slitted sheet I sit.

599 Is this your sister's sixth zither, Mister?

600 A laurel-crowned clown.

601 The local yokel yodels.

602 Many an anemone sees an enemy anemone.

Letters and Numbers

Riddles

603 What word is always spelled incorrectly?
Incorrectly.

604 What starts with a 'P', ends with an 'E', and has a million letters in it?
Post Office.

605 What ten-letter word starts with fuel?
Automobile.

606 What is the beginning of eternity, the end of time, and the beginning of every ending?
The letter 'E'.

607 When Adam introduced himself to Eve, which three words did he use that read the same backward and forward?

'Madam, I'm Adam.'

608 Two fathers and their sons go fishing. Each catches a fish, which is three in total. How is that possible?

The fishermen are a grandfather, father and son.

609 How many 2-cent stamps are in a dozen?

12. There are 12 of anything in a dozen.

610 What starts with an 'E', ends with an 'E', and only has one letter in it?

Envelope.

611 What word if pronounced right is wrong and if pronounced wrong is right?

Wrong.

612 What has four
fingers and a thumb
but is not a hand?
A glove.

613 Which letter of the
alphabet holds the
most water?
The 'C'.

614 Where does Friday come before Wednesday?
In the dictionary.

615 What's the centre of gravity?
The letter 'V'.

616 Which months have 28 days?
All of them.

617 **W**hat's the letter that ends everything?

The letter 'G'.

618 **N**ame three inventions that have helped man up in the world.

The elevator, the ladder and the alarm clock.

619 **W**hy is the Mississippi such an unusual river?

It has four 'I's and can't even see.

620 **H**ow many seconds are there in a year?

Twelve: 2nd of January, 2nd of February…

621 **W**hen does 'B' come after 'U'?

When you take some of its honey.

622 **W**hat's green, has eight legs and would kill you if it fell on you from out of a tree?

A billiard table.

623 **W**hat is the longest word in the world?

Smiles, because there is a mile between the beginning and the end.

624 **I** have ten legs, 20 arms and 54 feet. What am I?

A liar.

625 **W**hy can't a nose be more than 11 inches long?

If it was any longer it would be a foot.

626 **I**f Jill has 1.5 sand piles and Jesse has 2.5 sand piles and you combine them, how many sand piles would there be?

One.

627 **H**ow do you get four suits for a couple of dollars?

Buy a deck of cards.

628 **T**hree men were in a boat. It capsized but only two got their hair wet. Why?

The third man was bald.

629 **W**hat has a hundred legs but can't walk?

Fifty pairs of pants.

630 **W**hat's the hottest letter in the alphabet?

It's 'B', because it makes oil boil.

631 **W**hy was the maths book sad?

Because it had so many problems.

632 **W**hen do mathematicians die?

When their number is up.

633 **W**hat puzzles make you angry?

Crossword puzzles.

634 **W**hen does the alphabet only have 24 letters?

When 'U' and 'I' aren't there.

635 **W**hy was the baby pen crying?

Because its mum was doing a long sentence.

636 **I** make up all literature, but I'm often sealed. What am I?

Letters.

637 How do you make seven an even number?

Take off the 'S'.

638 Which animals are best at maths?

Rabbits, because they're always multiplying.

639 What word becomes shorter when you add two letters to it?

Short.

640 What occurs once in a minute, twice in a moment and never in a thousand years?

The letter 'M'.

641 What starts with 'T', ends with 'T' and has 'T' in it?

A teapot.

642 How do you make the number 'one' disappear?

Add a 'g' and it's 'gone'.

643 If two's company and three's a crowd, what are four and five?

Nine.

644 What has 88 keys but can't open a single door?

A piano.

645 What do the numbers 11, 69 and 88 have in common?

They all read the same upside-down.

646 When things go wrong, what can you always count on?

Your fingers.

647 If you took two apples from three apples, how many would you have?

The two you took.

648 What is at the end of the world?

The letter 'D'.

649 What did the zero say to the eight?

'I like your belt!'

650 How did the soccer fan know before the game that the score would be 0-0?

The score is always 0-0 before the game.

651 What has four legs but cannot walk?

A table.

652 **W**hy did the cat sit on the computer?

To keep an eye on the mouse.

653 **F**red has five daughters and each daughter has one brother. How many siblings are there?

Six. All five daughters have the same one brother.

654 **W**hat did the robber get when he stole a calendar?

12 months.

Only 355 days left before I can go back to the butcher shop for my next free calendar.

655 **H**ow many apples can you put in an empty box?

One. After that it's not empty anymore.

656 **W**hat bet can never be won?

The alphabet.

657 **W**hat has a hundred limbs but cannot walk?

A tree.

658 **W**hat is bigger when it's upside down?

The number 6.

659 **I**f I have it, I don't share it. If I share it, I don't have it. What is it?

A secret.

660 **W**hat was even more useful than the invention of the first telephone?

The second telephone.

661 **W**hy was number ten scared?

Because seven ate nine.

662 **W**hat is a forum?

One-um plus three-um.

663 **W**hat word is always spelled wrong?

Wrong.

664 **H**ow do you know when a spider is popular?

When it has its own website.

665 **Y**ou have a barrel of water and you need exactly one litre of water from it. How can you figure out one litre if you only have a 3L and a 5L container?

Fill the 3L container and pour into the 5L container. Fill the 3L again and fill the 5L from it. There will be one litre left in the 3L container.

666 The doctor gives you three tablets and tells you to take one every half hour. How long before you run out of tablets?

One hour. You take them at 0 mins, 30 mins and 1 hr.

667 How can "L" be greater in size than "XL"?

Roman numerals.

668 How do you share 32 apples evenly with 34 people?

Make apple sauce.

669 What do you call a man who shaves 15 times a day?

A barber.

670 If you toss a coin ten times and it lands heads-up every time, what are the chances it will land heads-up again the next time you toss it?

50%. Every time you toss the coin you have a 50% chance of getting heads.

671 How do you make a witch itch?

Take away the 'W'.

Tongue Twisters

672 One smart man felt smart. Two smart men felt smart. Three smart men felt smart. They all felt smart together.

673 The sixth sitting sheet slitter slit six sheets.

674 The tenth table tennis championship challenge.

675 Adam's attempted arithmetic answers were always error-riddled.

676 **T**wenty tenors tried tennis.

677 **S**ally spelled six synonyms.

678 **E**leven excited elves eagerly exited.

679 **F**ourteen fickle fairies failed flying.

680 **T**wo tooting toucans clap and tap too.

681 **S**ix hundred and sixty-seven sit-ups sent sick Steve spewing.

682 Seth said six sick spells. The six sick spells Seth said send Sheldon's silliness soaring. Silly Sheldon shouted sixty-six short spells. The sixty-six short spells Sheldon shouted ensured Seth suddenly ceased saying sick spells.

683 Sarah's sixth cycling session surely sucked.

684 The seventh ship sunk the sixth ship.

685 Sammie spent six Saturdays slouching silently on the sofa.

686 Eight mates eagerly wait for a really late date.

687 Ben sends ten hens to check on six sick sheep.

688 Eleven lemmings lend Lena eleven lemons.

689 Ten trumpeters triumphantly trumpeted.

Water Works

Riddles

690 **W**hen will water stop flowing downhill?

When it reaches the bottom.

691 **W**hy does the Statue of Liberty stand in New York Harbor?

Because it can't sit down.

The Statue of Liberty must have got tired and sat down...

692 **W**hat can be swallowed but can also swallow you?

Water.

693 **W**hat do you get if you jump into the Red Sea?

Wet.

694 **H**ow does a boat show its affection?
By hugging the shore?

695 **W**hat did the Pacific Ocean say to the Atlantic ocean?
Nothing, it just waved.

696 **W**hat's another word for tears?
Glumdrops.

697 **W**hat do you call a snowman with a suntan?
A puddle.

698 **H**ow do you saw the sea in half?
With a sea-saw.

699 **W**hat did one raindrop say to the other?

'Two's company, three's a cloud.'

700 **W**hat do you get if you cross the Atlantic with the Titanic?

About halfway.

701 **W**hy are rivers lazy?

Because they never get off their beds.

702 **W**hy does the ocean roar?

You would too if you had crabs on your bottom.

703 **W**hat goes through water but doesn't get wet?

A ray of light.

704 What do you call a ship that lies on the bottom of the ocean and shakes?

A nervous wreck.

705 What happened when the bell fell into the swimming pool?

It got wringing wet.

706 What washes up on very small beaches?

Microwaves.

707 What goes in pink and comes out blue?

A swimmer on a cold day.

708 **W**hat did the waterfall say to the fountain?

'You're just a little squirt.'

709 **W**hat is H2O4?

Drinking.

710 **I** go into water red and come out black what am I?

Hot metal.

711 **W**hat did the ground say to the rain?

'If this keeps up, I'll be mud.'

712 **W**hen a boy falls into the water, what is the first thing he does?

Gets wet.

713 **W**hat is round and deep but could not be filled up by all the water in the world?

A colander.

714 **W**hy can't it rain for two days in a row?

Because there is a night in between.

Tongue Twisters

715 **D**ripping tap, dip your hat.

716 **T**he big, silver, shiny ship sank.

717 **T**he stricken sinking sailor signalled SOS!

718 **B**oth blue boats brought bait but the boatmen borrowed Braydon's rods.

719 **I** see the sea is shining and the sun shimmers smartly.

720 **W**et Ron wrestled wringing wet Wally wrongly.

721 **W**rinkly Wally really wasted water.

722 **R**uby ran, rode and read by the wet river bed.

723 **R**uby waded in the raging white water river.

724 **A**lf frowned as he threw the anchor down.

725 **B**o's brother's boat broke.

726 **W**endy renders Ryan's wall when it's wet and rainy.

727 **A** splishy splashy fish was snatched by Mitch.

728 **F**unny Flo floundered while Fay found a floaty.

729 Simon swam and Netty snorkled.

730 Sam swam while Sim swallowed seawater.

731 Splish, splash, swish, squished fish.

732 Blake blew blue bubbles in the bath.

733 Slim Shauna's sure she can swim to shore.

734 Doug dips, slides, slips and dives.

735 **B**ackstroke and breaststroke are both a breeze.

736 **S**himmering Swiss swimmers shimmer.

737 **S**ammy sat on a sandy shore and is sure her shorts are sandy.

738 **S**teve is a slave to the slow wet waves.

739 **W**ater sports see Spiro sporting spotty board shorts.

Strange School and Wacky Work

Riddles

740 **W**hy do firemen wear red braces?
To keep their trousers up.

741 **W**ho gets the sack every time he goes to work?
The postman.

742 **W**hat's black when it's clean and white when it's dirty?
A blackboard.

743 **I**f a butcher is two metres tall and has size eleven feet, what does he weigh?
Meat.

744 **W**hy was the archaeologist upset?

Because his job was in ruins!

745 **W**hy do doctors wear masks when operating?

Because if they make a mistake nobody will know who did it.

746 **W**hat did the burglar say to the lady who caught him stealing her silver?

'I'm at your service, Ma'am.'

747 **W**hat did the dentist say to the golfer?

'You've got a hole in one!'

748 **W**hy couldn't the sailors play cards?

The captain was standing on the deck.

749 **W**hy are cooks mean?

Because they beat eggs and whip cream!

750 **W**hat's the difference between a jeweller and a jailer?

A jeweller sells watches and a jailer watches cells.

751 **W**hy can't anyone stay angry with actors?

Because they always make up.

752 **W**hat did the farmer say when he lost his tractor?

'Where's my tractor?'

753 **W**hy did the boy laugh after his operation?

Because the doctor had him in stitches.

754 **W**hy didn't the boy work in the wool factory?

Because he was too young to dye.

755 **W**hy did the farmer plough his field with a steamroller?

He wanted to grow mashed potatoes.

756 **A** teacher, a builder and a hat maker were walking down the street. Who had the biggest hat?

The one with the biggest head.

757 **W**hat is the difference between a bus driver and a cold?

One knows the stops, the other stops the nose.

758 **W**hat time do most people go to the dentist?

Tooth-hurty.

759 What illness do retired pilots get?

Flu.

760 How did the dentist become a brain surgeon?

His drill slipped.

761 How did the comedian pass the time in hospital?

By telling sick jokes.

762 What type of music do geologists like best?

Rock.

763 How can you tell an undertaker?

By his grave manner.

764 **W**hy do artists make a lot of money?

Because they can draw their own wages.

765 **H**ow do fisherman make nets?

They make lots of holes and tie them together with string.

766 **W**hat did the dentist want?

The tooth, the whole tooth and nothing but the tooth.

767 **W**hat's red, white and brown and travels faster than the speed of sound?

An astronaut's ham and tomato sandwich.

768 **W**hat is a computer's first sign of old age?

It loses its memory.

769 What do you get when you cross a plumber with a ballerina?

A tap dancer.

770 Why did the computer sneeze?

It had a virus.

771 What's the difference between a train station and a teacher?

One minds the train, the other trains the mind.

772 Why couldn't the boy go straight home from school?

Because he lived around the corner.

773 What is the easiest way to get a day off school?

Wait until Saturday.

774 **W**hy was the cross-eyed teacher so frustrated?

Because he couldn't control his pupils.

775 **W**hat trees do fortune tellers look at?

Palms.

776 **I** sometimes build bridges of silver and crowns of gold. Who am I?

A dentist.

777 **W**hat's the difference between a nightwatchman and a butcher?

One stays awake and the other weighs a steak.

778 **W**hen is homework no longer homework?
When you hand it in to the teacher.

779 **W**hat is a robot's favourite part of the school day?
Assembly.

780 **W**hy was the computer so tired when it got home?
Because it had a hard drive.

781 **W**hy do artists never win at sports?
They keep drawing.

Tongue Twisters

782 The assistant principal's announcement signalled silence.

783 Steven suddenly stopped serious science study.

784 Leisel learned lots of lessons at lunchtime.

785 Suspension, expulsion, detention, yard duty.

786 Clara took glasses in cases to class. Clara carelessly cracked glasses in classes. Clara's cracked glasses in cases in classes caused chaos.

787 Aaron, Alex and Arwin arrived at after-school care all alone.

788 Trudy was tardy attending trigonometry; trigonometry truly was a trial for Trudy.

789 Leroy liked learning literature.

790 Peter played politely in the playground at playtime.

791 Henrietta's horribly hard history homework was hysterical.

792 Sirius's sister's slackness ensured slowly slipping science scores.

793 Frank finally passed physics after frequently failing.

794 Truant Tracey's truancy tricked teachers.

795 Geography is generally geographic.

796 The maths course was massively maths based.

797 Cheating Cameron continuously copied Chelsea till checking teacher caught Cameron cheating, causing Cameron to cop a caning.

798 Elizabeth Hanson studies studiously.

799 Steven's lunch bag seriously stank.

800 Sick Steven skipped school.

801 Teaching trigonometry is tricky.

802 Danny's detention definitely dragged.

803 Recess rocks!

804 Is this a mystical mist myth, Miss?

805 Salesman Stan's shop stocks short spotted socks.

806 Terry told the teacher to try talking tougher.

807 Detention helped Rita's attention retention.

808 Polly' shirt shop sold pre-shrunk silk shirts.

Freaky Food

Riddles

809 **W**hy don't bananas get lonely?

Because they hang around in bunches.

810 **H**ow do you make a potato puff?

Chase it around the garden.

811 **W**hat do you get when you cross a baby rabbit with a vegetable?

A bunion.

812 **W**hat are two things you cannot have for breakfast?

Lunch and dinner.

813 **W**hat kind of room has no door, no windows, no floor and no roof?

A mushroom.

814 **W**hat's the difference between a young lady and a fresh loaf?

One is a well-bred maid and the other is well-made bread.

815 **W**hat has to be broken before you have use it?

An egg.

816 **O**n what nuts can pictures hang?

Walnuts.

817 **W**hich cheese is made backwards?

Edam.

818 **W**hat do you get when you cross and orange with a squash court?

Orange squash.

819 **H**ow do you make a banana split?

Cut it in half.

820 **W**hat kind of cup can't hold water?

A cupcake.

821 **W**hat vegetable goes well with jacket potatoes?

Button mushrooms.

822 **W**hat did one tomato say to the other that was lagging behind?

'Ketchup!'

823 **W**hat did the egg say to the whisk?

'I know when I'm beaten.'

824 **W**hat's green, sad and covered in custard?

Apple grumble.

Where all the slow tomatoes end up.

Oh! What a miserable pudding!

GRUMBLE GRUMBLE GRUMBLE

825 **W**hat do you get if you cross a cowboy with a stew?

Hopalong Casserole.

826 **H**ow do you make a hot dog stand?

Steal its chair.

827 **W**ho swings through the cake shop, yodelling?

Tarzipan.

828 **W**hy is orange juice so smart?

It concentrates.

829 **W**hy are teddy bears never hungry?

Because they are always stuffed.

830 **I**f you have a referee in football, what do you have in bowls?

Cornflakes.

831 **D**id Adam and Eve have a date?

No, they had an apple.

832 **W**hat can you serve but never eat?

A tennis ball.

833 **W**hat's small, white, round and giggles?

A tickled onion.

834 **W**hat do you call two rows of vegetables?

A dual cabbageway.

835 **W**hat type of jam can't you eat?

A traffic jam.

836 **W**hy are sausages so bad mannered?

They spit in the frying pan.

837 **W**hy do watermelons get married?

Because they can't-elope.

838 **W**here were potatoes first found?

In the ground.

839 **W**hat is the difference between a hungry person and a greedy person?

One longs to eats and the other eats too long.

840 **W**hat did one potato chip say to the other?

'Shall we go for a dip?'

841 When do you go when red but stop when green?

When eating a watermelon.

842 Why is milk the fastest thing in the world?

Because it's pasteurised before you see it.

843 What side of an apple is the left side?

The side that hasn't been eaten.

844 What happened when there was a fight in the fish and chip shop?

Two fish got battered.

Tongue Twisters

845 Chop shops stock chops.

846 A proper copper coffee pot.

847 The kitchen cutlery clattered and clunked.

848 The chunky chef got charred cooking.

849 Samantha slipped on thick, sloppy sauce.

850 Corey's cooking class clapped Cara's crumble.

851 Practise proper pancake preparation to promise pristinely prepared perfect pancakes.

852 Greasy, grimy grills gladdened Gareth.

853 Silly Susan stirred a saucepan of spicy, steaming spinach soup with a spatula.

854 Arthur halved hairy Harry's hash brown.

855 Four flattened French fries.

856 How many cans can Cam cram in a curry?

857 Fran loved fried flan.

858 Greg's gluggy gravy got gloopy.

859 Frank frustratingly flipped forks. Frank's fork finally ferociously flipped.

860 Swiss watch, Swiss cheese.

861 'Better bring better butter, Betty!' Barry bellowed. Betty bawled, berating Barry for bringing better butter. 'Bother,' Betty's brother blackly breathed.

862 Bunny's bananas burned and Vinny blamed blurry vision.

863 Sally's slippery serving spoon slipped while serving salad.

864 Betty blew raspberries while Bonny bit blueberries.

865 Fritz's fired pizza and Percy's fried fish were fresh.

Silly Stuff

Riddles

866 **W**hat has a bottom at the top?
A leg.

867 **W**hat kind of star wears sunglasses?
A movie star.

868 **W**hy is a ladies' belt like a garbage truck?
Because it goes around and gathers the waist.

869 **W**hat invention allows you to see through walls?
A window.

870 **W**hy did the boy sit on his watch?

He wanted to be on time.

871 **W**hat needs to be answered, but doesn't ask a question?

A telephone.

872 **W**here was Solomon's temple?

On his head.

873 **W**hy did the girl tear a page out of the calendar?

Because she wanted to take a month off.

874 **W**hy did the boy put his bed in the fireplace?

So he could sleep like a log.

875 **W**hy do we dress baby girls in pink and baby boys in blue?

Because they can't dress themselves.

Obviously radical babies

876 **W**hich is the longest rope?

Europe.

877 **W**hat is always behind the times?

The back of a watch.

878 **W**hat does a girl look for but hopes she never finds?

A ladder in her pantyhose.

Oh no! I've laddered my pantyhose!

879 **W**hat's easy to get into but hard to get out of?

Trouble.

880 **W**here can you always find a helping hand?

At the end of your arm.

881 **W**hat's the definition of intense?

That's where campers sleep.

882 **W**hat did the shoe say to the foot?

'You're having me on.'

883 **W**hy are false teeth like stars?

They come out at night.

884 **W**hy did the belt go to jail?

Because it held up a pair of pants.

885 **W**hat did the stamp say to the envelope?

'Stick with me and we'll go places.'

886 **H**ow does a fireplace feel?

Grate!

887 **W**hat's the difference between and oak tree and a tight pair of shoes?

One makes acorns, the other makes corns ache.

888 **W**hat do you get when you cross a frog and a hare?

A bunny ribbit!

889 **W**hat did one wall say to the other wall?

'I'll meet you at the corner.'

890 **C**an February March?

No, but April May.

891 **W**hen is a chair like a woman's dress?

When it's satin.

892 **W**hat did the tie say to the hat?

'You go on ahead, I'll just hang around.'

893 **H**ow long should a person's legs be?

Long enough to reach their feet.

894 **W**hat do hippies do?

They hold your leggies on.

895 **W**hat did the pencil sharpener say to the pencil?

'Stop going in circles and get to the point!'

896 **H**ow do you make a pair of trousers last?

Make the coat first.

897 **C**an a match box?

No, but a tin can.

898 **W**hy did the traffic light turn red?

You would too if you had to change in the middle of the street!

899 **W**hat did the little mountain say to the big mountain?

'Hi Cliff!'

900 **W**here are the Andes?

At the end of your armies.

901 **W**hen is the cheapest time to phone friends?

When they're not home.

902 **W**hat did the big hand of the clock say to the little hand?

'Got a minute?'

903 **W**hat flowers grow under your nose?

Tulips.

904 **W**hat did the key say to the glue?

'You wanna be in show biz, kid? Stick to me, I can open up doors for you!'

905 **W**hat did the first mind reader say to the second mind reader?

'You're all right, how am I?'

906 **W**hat sort of star is dangerous?

A shooting star.

907 **W**hich trees are always sad?

Pine trees.

908 **H**ow do you make fire with two sticks?
Make sure one of them is a match.

909 **W**hat is the only true cure for dandruff?
Baldness!

910 **W**hat did the didgeridoo?
Answered the phone when the boomerang.

911 **W**hat did the piece of wood say to the drill?
You bore me.

912 **I** have every colour but no gold, what am I?
A rainbow.

913 **W**hy did the car get a puncture?

There was a fork in the road.

914 **W**hat dance do hippies hate?

A square dance.

915 **W**hen do clocks die?

When their time's up.

916 **W**hat's green and short and goes camping?

A boy sprout.

917 **W**hat's the easiest way to find a pin in your carpet?

Walk around in bare feet.

918 **W**hat did the big chimney say to the little chimney?

'You're too young to smoke.'

919 **W**hat's the easiest way to get on TV?

Sit on it.

920 **W**hat did the big telephone say to the little telephone?

'You're too young to be engaged.'

921 **W**hy do you go to bed?

Because the bed will not come to you.

922 **I**f everyone bought a white car, what would we have?

A white carnation.

923 **W**hy is a bride always out of luck on her wedding day?

Because she never marries the best man.

924 **W**hy did the one-armed man cross the road?

He wanted to get to the second-hand shop.

925 **W**hich organ is the only one to have named itself?

The brain.

926 **Y**ou use me from your head to your toes, the more I work the thinner I grow. What am I?

A bar of soap.

927 **W**here are English kings and queens crowned?

On the head.

928 **W**hat do you call a lazy toy?

An inaction figure.

929 **H**ow do you catch a squirrel?

Climb into a tree and act like a nut.

930 **W**hat's the definition of minimum?

A very small mother.

931 **W**hy do toadstools grow so close together?

They don't need mushroom.

932 **W**hy was the broom late?

It overswept.

933 What are government workers called in Spain?

Seville servants.

934 Why did the bacteria cross the microscope?

To get to the other slide.

935 What has a neck but no head?

A bottle.

936 How often do Christmas Day and New Year's day fall in the same year?

Every year.

937 What do you call a man with a map on his head?

Miles!

938 What do you call a man with a spade?

Doug.

939 What do you call a man without a spade?

Douglas!

940 What do you call a man pouring water into a jug?

Phil.

941 What do you call a lady in the middle of a tennis court?

Annette.

942 What do you call a woman with one leg?

Eileen.

943 What do you call a
girl with a frog on her
head?

Lily.

944 What do you call a
man covered in cat
scratches?

Claude.

945 What do you call a
man in a pile of leaves?

Russell.

946 What do you call a man with rabbits in his pants?

Warren.

947 What's brown and sticky?

A stick.

948 What's the coldest country in the world?
Chile.

949 What kind of song can you sing in the car?
A cartoon (car tune).

950 Why did the girl throw her guitar away?
Because it had a hole in the middle.

951 Why does lighting shock people?
It doesn't know how to conduct itself.

952 What can you sit on, sleep on and brush your hair with?
A chair, a bed and a hairbrush.

953 **W**hat moves faster, heat or cold?

Heat. Anyone can catch a cold.

954 **H**ow do you use an Egyptian doorbell?

Toot-and-come-in.

955 **W**hat is always the tallest building in a town?

The library. It has a lot of stories.

956 **W**hy did the boy bury his torch?

The batteries died.

957 **W**here did the king keep his armies?

Up his sleevies.

958 **W**hy did the snowman dress up?

Because he was going to the snowball.

959 **I**f a purple man lives in a purple house and a yellow man lives in a yellow house, who lives in the Whitehouse?

The President of the USA.

960 **I** am red, green, blue and purple and nobody can reach me – not even a giant. What am I?

A rainbow.

961 **W**hat did the alien say to the petrol pump?

'Take you finger out of your ear when I'm talking to you.'

962 What do all the Smiths in the phonebook have in common?

They all have phones.

963 What turns into a different story?

A spiral staircase.

964 I have all of your knowledge but could fit in your hands. What am I?

Your brain.

965 What do you call a boomerang that doesn't come back to you?

A stick.

966 What am I?

A question.

967 In what month do people sleep the least?

February because it's the shortest month.

968 Why was the Egyptian girl worried?

Because her daddy was a mummy.

969 What has a foot but no leg?

A ruler.

Tongue Twisters

970 **A**udrey ought to let slight slips go.

971 **I**rish wristwatch, Swiss wristwatch.

SWISS
WRISTWATCH

IRISH
WRISTWATCH

972 **O**llie's orange organ.

973 **P**rincess Pauline, the pretty pianist, prettily played piano.

974 Greg's grimy gooey green glockenspiel.

975 A particularly pleasant, playful Pop played pleasantly.

976 The sliding door silently slid softly shut.

977 Peter played pretty perfect piano.

978 Shane's shuttlecock shattered, sending Shane insane.

979 Cameron cruelly cut Christopher's crew cut, causing Christopher to cry.

980 Patiently practising picking, plucking, playing guitar.

981 Faith faces faithfully west. Facing west, Faith faced friends fighting.

982 Every excellent egg easily excelled at exaggerating.

983 Bryan's a bald but buffed boxer.

984 Right or wrong, white nights are right.

985 The big blue beanbag broke, blasting billions of beans backward.

986 An accuser alleged Randal's actions as absolutely unacceptable.

987 Can you can a can as a canner can can a can?

988 Tiny Tim thought trippy thoughts.

Tiptoe through the tulips with me!

989 **A**ctive Adam asked Akmal for answers.

990 **S**ix short slow shepherds.

991 **C**lever Kelly gasps and clasps the glass cask.

992 **S**ome shun sunshine.

993 **T**hree free throws.

994 A truly frugal ruler's mural.

995 When does the watch shop shut?

996 Susie sat in a shoe shine shop. Where she shines she sits and where she sits she shines.

997 Fearful Frankie thought fully frightening thoughts.

998 Clean clams crammed in clean cans.

999 When does Wendy whine about the World Wide Web?

1000 Sure the ship's shipshape, sir.

1001 Wayne really watches walruses in rural Wales.